HAVE A
NICE DAY!

HAVE A NICE DAY!

HOW MODERN LIFE DRIVES YOU MAD

ADAM DANT

REDSTONE PRESS

CONTENTS

INTRODUCTION BY EMMA TENNANT

This is the kind of book that only crops up once in a generation: a subtle, witty look at what it's like to be alive today, the setbacks, false dawns and piercing *aperçus* which lead us all to wonder what exactly IS wrong with modern life, when so much of its moods and products are billed with rapture. We've never had it so good - or are we victims of a giant hoax? Why is it so clear to so many that modern life is driving us mad?

Adam Dant is the artist who brings the side-splitting reality of our predicament home to roost. Like Thurber and Bateman before him, he sums up the sheer agony of existence, the 'it's so awful you have to laugh' centre of madness we have to live with - but, belonging as he does to the here-and-now, he makes use of a cartoon, graphic-novel approach and shows us as bewildered denizens of a Utopia where nothing works and we are all reduced to identical, faceless consumers. In the ever-rolling storyboard of his achingly funny art, we understand at last why modern life drives us mad.

Note: HAVE A NICE DAY! is inspired by a famous test devised by the psychologist Saul Rosenzweig (the Rosenzweig picture-frustration study). The Harvard Professor wished to measure a person's latent aggression in frustrating situations. The original series showed images of two characters in a given scenario, each with a speech bubble. One of the characters says something that is obviously enraging while the other bubble is left blank for the subjects response.

EXCUSE ME! I'M DOING A PICTURE BOOK CALLED 'FREAK-BOY' & I WONDERED......

OUT AND ABOUT

I'M NOT BEING RUDE PUSHING IN FRONT OF YOU! I JUST DON'T WANT TO GET STUCK HERE IF YOU GET JAMMED IN THE DOOR!

YES! I KNOW YOU SAID SHORT BACK & SIDES BUT I THOUGHT A NUMBER 2 WOULD LOOK BETTER

MANNERS

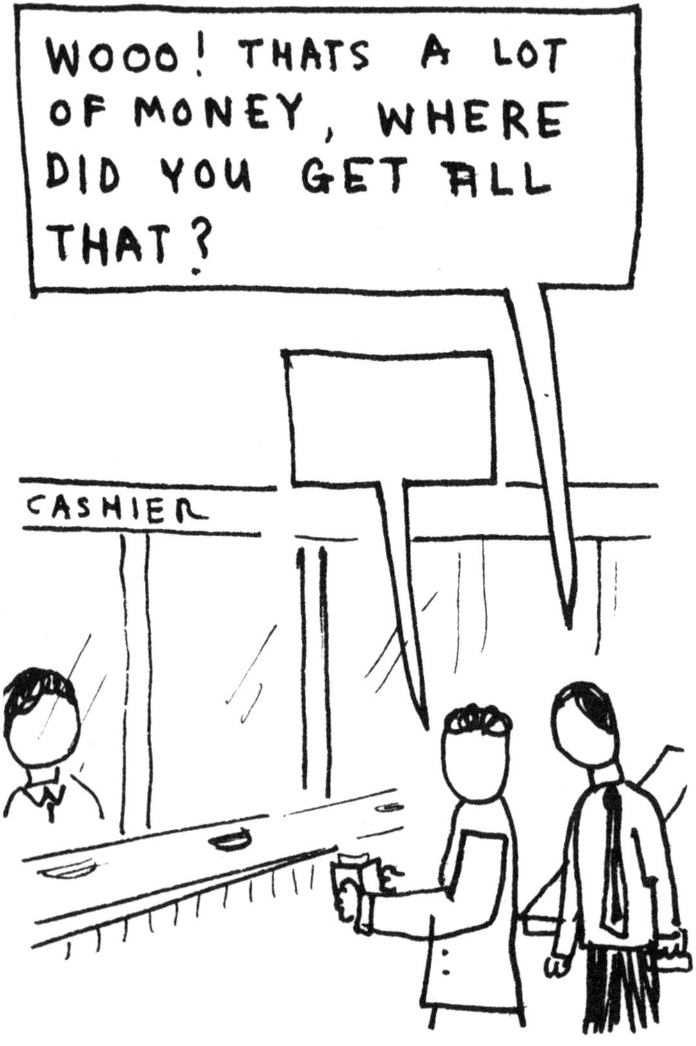
WOOO! THATS A LOT OF MONEY, WHERE DID YOU GET ALL THAT?
CASHIER

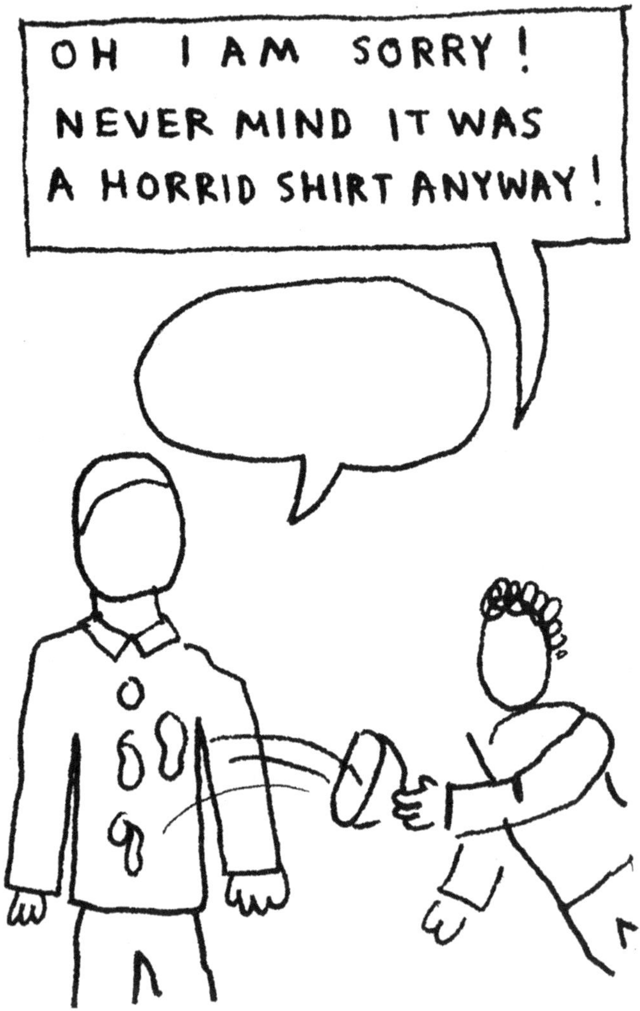
OH I AM SORRY! NEVER MIND IT WAS A HORRID SHIRT ANYWAY!

OTHER PEOPLE

I LOVE WHAT YOU'VE DONE WITH THE LIVING ROOM, HAVE YOU EVER VISITED THE SLUMS IN CALCUTTA?

GENERAL VIOLENCE

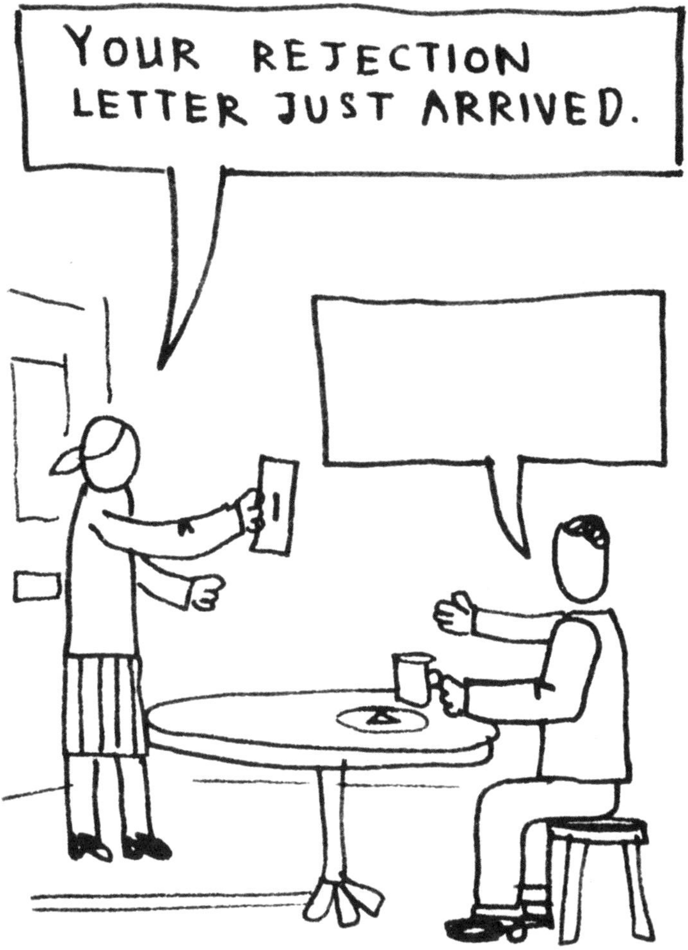
YOUR REJECTION LETTER JUST ARRIVED.

KNOWLEDGE

EXCUSE ME BUT WHEN YOU SAY 'QUESTIONS FROM THE FLOOR' DO YOU MEAN US OR THE ACTUAL FLOOR?
HIGHER LEARNING

SELECTIVE MEMORY

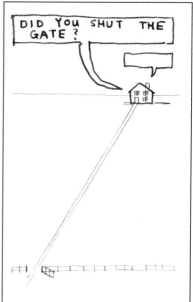

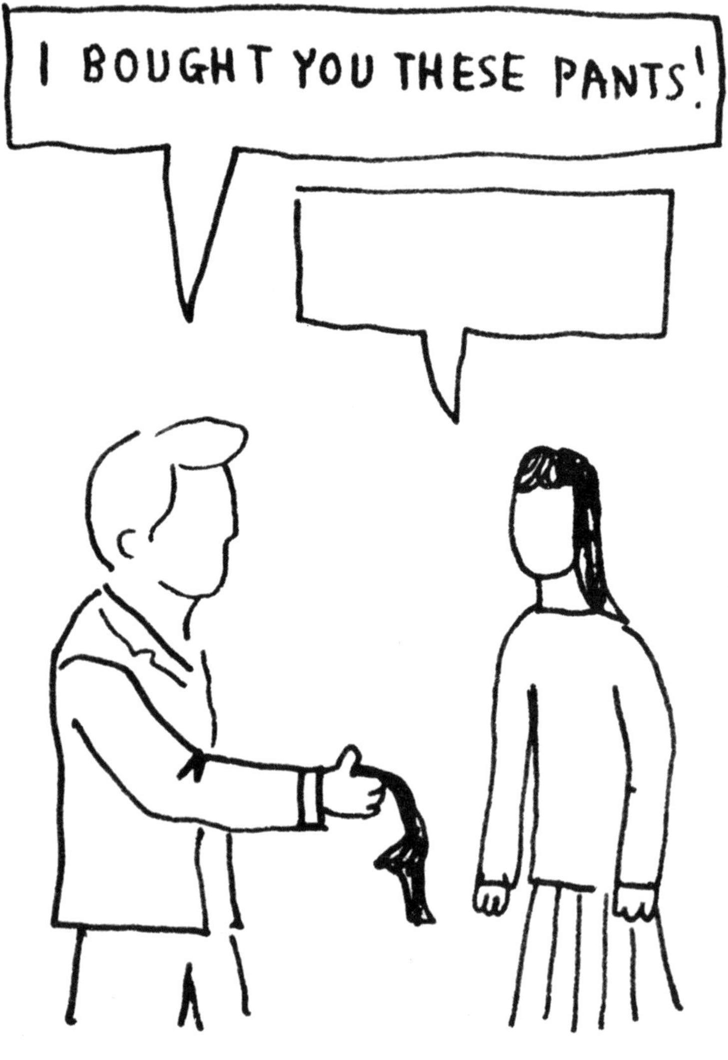
I BOUGHT YOU THESE PANTS!

RELATIONSHIPS

51

TRAFFIC

FAMILY LIFE

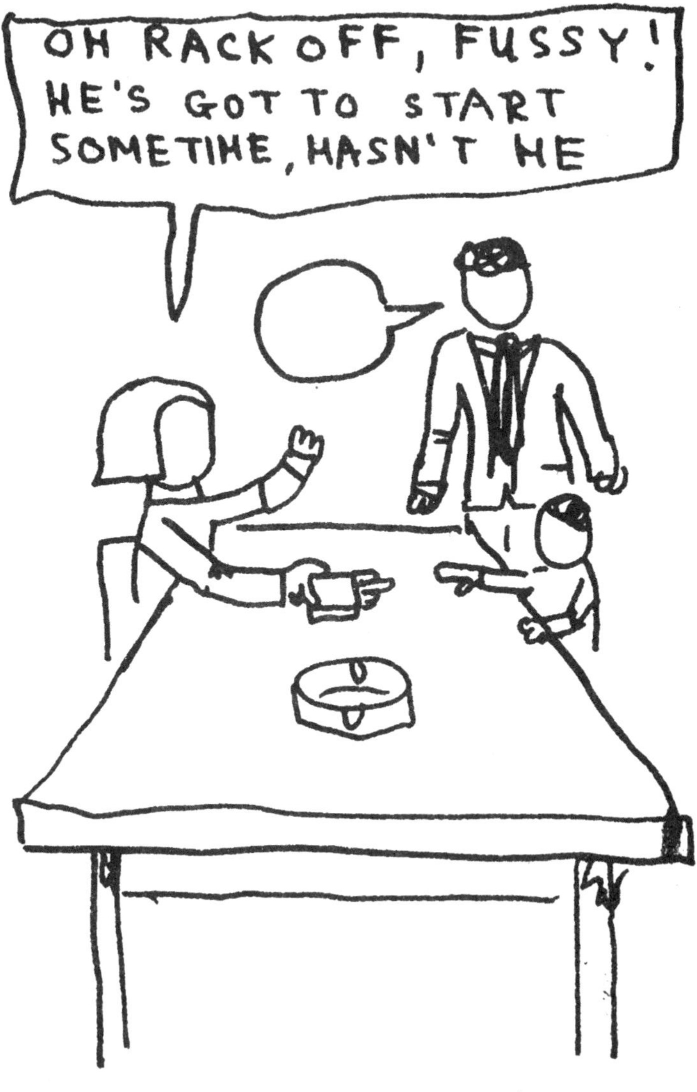
OH RACK OFF, FUSSY!
HE'S GOT TO START
SOMETIME, HASN'T HE

DIGESTION

THANKS FOR COMING SO SOON DOCTOR, THERE'S SUPER-GLUE JUST EVERYWHERE!

HEALTH

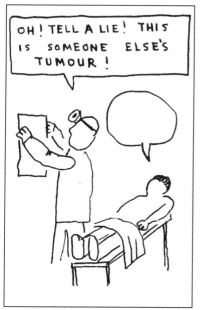

PRODUCTS

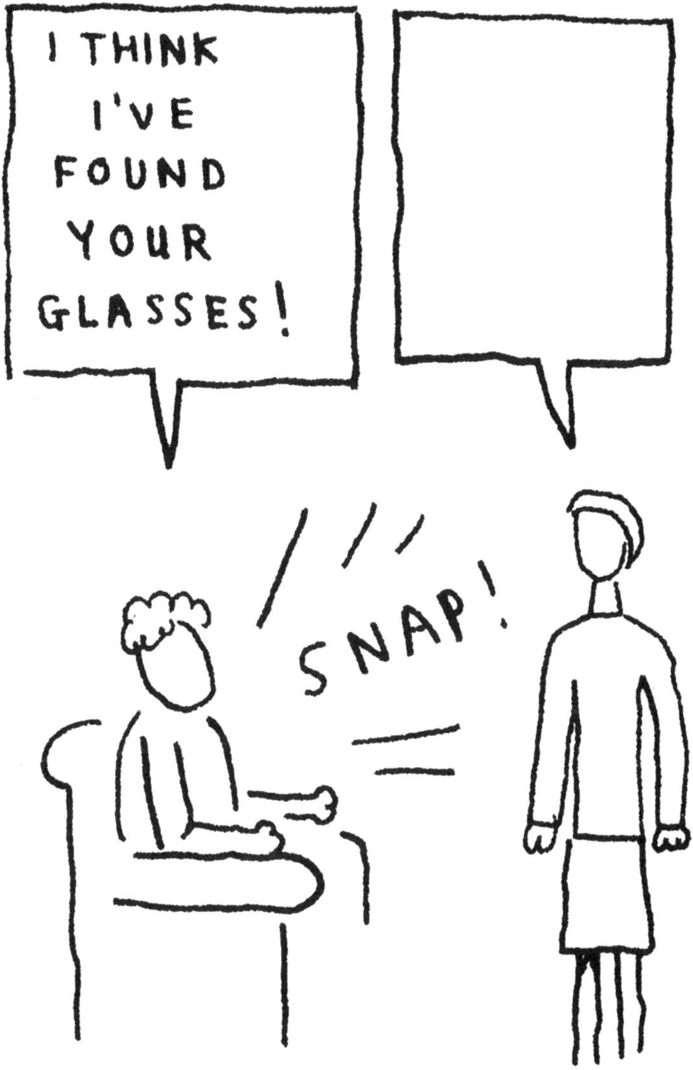
I THINK I'VE FOUND YOUR GLASSES!
SNAP!

MODERN LIFE

ON HOLIDAY

AUSTRALIAN? AREN'T THEY THE SLUTTY ONES WITH NO CULTURE, DRESS SENSE OR SELF CONTROL?

APPENDIX

ADDITIONAL CHARGES

IN OPENING THIS LETTER YOU HAVE AGREED TO THE FOLLOWING

Envelope servicing, filling & sealing	£2·00
Postage stamp drawer space occupation levy	£0·50
Postage stamp glue insurance premium	£0·50
(covers adhesion failure and illness due to gum allergy, does not cover perforation damage or any charges resulting from such)	
Desk to postbox carriage charge	£1·50
Optional first class supplement	£ ·50
Early collection supplement	£1·00
Charge for running to catch post-office collection van at post pox	£2·00
Street-dog avoidance payment	£0·50
Shoe-leather & lace wear % charge	£0·40
Return address inclusion fee	£0·40
Paper-cut insurance	£0·50
Full-post-box-eventuality charge	£1·00
(covers possibility of stalled first visits to post-box)	
Foreign word comprehension levy	£2·00
(includes dictionary bookshelf space occupation levy for condensed editions 40% extra for full hardcover)	
Umbrella use & storage fee	£1·00
TOTAL DUE	£14·80

INDEX OF EXEMPTIONS
YOUR POLICY IS INEFFECTUAL IN CASES OF THE FOLLOWING

INJURIES SUSTAINED WHILST DISTRACTING MUSIC IS PRESENT (INCLUDING BUSKERS AND CERTAIN BIRDSONG & WHISTLING)

ALL ILLNESSESS THAT HAVE NO EQUIVILENT SUITABLE TRANSLATION IN THE GERMAN LANGUAGE

ALL FOLK DISEASES

TRI-CYCLE RELATED INJURIES

DISEASES CONTRACTED IN BUILT-UP AREAS WHERE ADJACENT BUILDINGS ARE BETWEEN 12 & 34 FLOORS TALL.

ILLNESSES CONTRACTED IN BANKS & BUILDING SOCIETIES.

SEMI-SERIOUS GRAZES SUFFERED BY VISITORS TO CERTAIN STATELY HOMES (SEE OUR HOLIDAY BREAK CATALOGUE)

SEXUAL PROBLEMS SUFFERED BY SUBSCRIBERS TO OUR HOLIDAY BREAK CATALOGUE)

FLUTE & DRUM MARCHING WHELTS

PROBLEMS POLICY HOLDERS HAVE CONCEALED FROM THEIR POSTMAN, MILKMAN, BINMAN (EXCLUDES METER-READERS AND COURIERS)

INJURIES ARISING FROM MISUSE OF WATER

LETTUCE/MARMITE COMBINATION DIET INCIDENCE

SNAIL RELATED INJURIES.

INJURIES SUSTAINED DURING SUPERHERO IMPERSONATIONS (DOES NOT APPLY IN INCIDENCES WHERE COMIC-BOOK FIGURES EXIST WITHOUT FILM ADAPTATION EQUIVILENT EXCEPT IN CASES OF ANIMAL SUPER-HEROS)

MISHAPS WHERE VICTIM IS KNOWN TO HAVE BEEN SHOUTING

SLIPPING ON RAW EGGS (UNSHELLED)

WOODCARVING INJURIES SUSTAINED WHILST CREATING NON-FIGURATIVE OBJECTS

INJURIES SUSTAINED WHILST WEARING ANY FORM OF ANTIQUE, VINTAGE OR NOSTALGIC CLOTHING (SEE NOTES ON FLARES & CORSET SUR-CHARGES)

CUTS RESULTING FROM LEFT-HAND GUITARISTS ATTEMPTING TO PLAY RE-STRUNG RIGHT-HANDED GUITARS.

INJURY RESULTING FROM STUPIDITY

ILLNESSESS CONTRACTED FROM HOARDING OF OLD BITS OF CLOTH

"£EATOWT"
THE NEW DINING CONTRACT
the Menu

To Commence~
- Waffled lung
- Street Artichokes
- Triple rinsed lettuce glass
- Traditional Whore Brandy
- Masticated Spanish gravel radish
- Sprouts from 4 corners of the field
- Trans continent tidbits
- Mouth parts

Platters ~
- Piano flattened rabbit on a bed of living ivy fluviated by a white south London Jus.
- A bevy of child sized aquatic forms in spring formation
- Congested beef and cress crest
- Bicycle seat shaped cutlet on realistic mash
- Arse of the day
- 'It used to be a chicken ™'
- Hand numbered sprats
- climbing rat of portugal

Deserts ~
- Edible poker hand

a 17·5% compulsory guilt charge will be added to your bill

COURT & SOCIAL & OTHER

LARGE PALACE

His Excellency Ciao Ciao Robertson and the Mrs Robertson led a delegation of partially serious tradesmen around the back of the palace to be 'done' in a right royal fashion. They bade farewell in a Saint Johns ambulance

Forthcoming marriages

The centre forward of **our triumphant rovers** will **marry the curly haired ginger one** from 'Gals mit tuens'

The engagement is announced between Colin, the yoghurt heir andagentleman and Susan, 'just another Susan', **Pullover.**

Weddings

Mr F. James and Miss P. Clop
Their marriage took place after a very long trip up an extremely long aisle.

Births

Astronaut – on 16th to **Panda** (née Argument) and Henceforth, a son, Astrolabe, Astrocat, a brother for Marigold, Addis.

Cucumber – on 16th to Crabmayo (née Nettles) and Codloin a daughter, Mint, a sister for linen and Chesterfield

Car – on 16th to Beep Beep (née Bike) and Van a couple or so of kids, van II & III or truck II a rival and sparring partner for O.B 1

Death

None

Thanks

Thanks Tim Thanksa lots.

Dinner

Dinner will be served at about 7 pm

CULTURAL DIFFERENCES YOU MUST OBSERVE

When crossing the road in larger cities it is traditional to salute tractors.

Cravats must be donned in the presence of statues depicting our glorious leader.

Always queue from the right.

Do not ask for turkey-dishes in restaurants as it is our esteemed national bird & we cannot get it anyway as it lives too far away.

It is considered impolite to stand near a lady who has a headache.

You are not permitted to sneeze during the playing of the national anthem

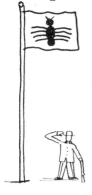

Cash cannot be used to buy matches or eggs.

Taxi drivers are forbidden from bathing at weekends.

Skis must not be carried into Railway station.
It is illegal to kiss currency.
Foreign visitors are not permitted to eat some local dishes.

UNUSUAL BABY NAMES (UNI-SEX)

AG
Asolia
Androgyna
Aieeeeee
Alibut

Bozo
Bowel
Brabbit

Coin
Cranny
Cor
Crumpskein
Coilet

Dwagbut
Dôgstaine

Egsmel

Fat
Fuekulope
Fanston
Foolishwa

Gutso
Gazpot
Grababitt
Gav

Henpot
Hoolioupe
Hrnge
Hospíp

Inge
I
Imâpra
Istleto

Jakster
Jampot
Junipoo

kök
knöeb
knusty

Lubster
Lucy
Loin
Lacbrane

Malcub
Mossiface
MMMM
Mooner
Miliprik
Mountain

Nigeographe

Oland
Ostopop
Oglesnout

Pinknosina
Prapforth
pelicoptr

Quazzer
Qumpy
Questioneeria

spot
Spoe
spoonfediolica
sexpistolia

Truck II
Transpalcolm
Torid

Uzbud
Ulikeme

Vag
Vanisher

Wud
Wagony
Wagmium.

RELATED NEWSPAPER ARTICLES

MODERN LABOR
NO LET UP IN CITI-WIDE PROTECTED BAT INFESTATION WRANGLE

HI!
MAN GOES COMPLETELY BERSERK!

WHAT
PRICE TO GO UP + UP

THE SON
VICTORY FOR SOCK-WEARERS IN 27 YEAR LONG, STUPID VERY EXPENSIVE + POINTLESS LEGAL BATTLE

THE WAD
PENIS 'VIRTUALLY USE LESS' DEEM TOP DOCS

NEW 'CREAM AT BOTTOM OF BOTTLE' MILKBOTTLE AVAILABLE BY MID-DEC.

THE NEW
PONIES POSE TERRIBLE NEW DANGER

BLACK OUT
TAX ON IDENTITY NOW A CERTAINTY

THE WRECKER
NEW CURRENCY DESIGN NUMBERS UNINTELLIGIBLE

DAILY DOUGH
WE USED WRONG GLUE! ADMIT WORRIED SURGEONS

HOLY NEWS
DINER DISCOVERS NEW TASTE

TOWN
LACK OF WHEELS LEADS TO TRANSPORT FOUL UP

OPERATION EXTREME HANDSHAKE

OPERATION MOTHER IS ITALIAN

OPERATION RELIGIOUS TYPE JUSTICE

OPERATION HATE + KILL

OPERATION JUST KILL

OPERATION KILL, KILL, KILL

OPERATION STABBITY

OPERATION ENDLESS RETRIBUTION

OPERATION TEA-TIME

OPERATION CHICKEN-WIPE-OUT

OPERATION MY HEART WILL GO ON

OPERATION UNLIMITED LOVE THREAT

TICKET PRICING STRUCTURE CLARIFICATION

WEEKDAY PASSENGERS WHO HOLD A TUESDAY TO FRIDAY FORTNIGHTLY RE-NEWABLE FLEX-TRAVEL $8/17ths\%$ discount 'HOP-AWAY' PASS MUST USE IT ON EVERY OTHER WEDNESDAY FOR JOURNEYS ON THE INTER-URBAN DIRECT 8 CARRIAGE FLYER SERVICE IN CONJUNCTION WITH THE LEISURE-LOSER MID-DAY BUDGETEER PROMOTION, EXCEPT ON 'TUESDAY TEA-TIME SPECIAL' TRAINS AND DURING APRIL WHEN AN ADDITIONAL $3/8ths$ OF THE UPPER-CLASS LUNCHING FARE WILL ENABLE TRAVEL IN EXEMPLARY CLASS ACCOMODATION (EXCLUDING $23/38ths$ SUPPLIMENT FOR 'TOFF-DINNER' SERVICE IN THE DINING CAR — ADEQUATE SEATING PROVIDING).

USEFUL PHRASES

At Hotel / Atotel

The matress is filled with lice	IL Monto ist mid flign-flagn gevol.
The curtains are afire	IL Mantimontomintimanti ist smom smom smom.
The carpet is sodden with old urine.	IL tappy mid pim-pim ist geJussy.
Your waiter just assaulted our 6year old son.	Bir pingo hav hutter-nitter snippendipinned.
Where is the emergency saw	ooh hu zûzû ingerJinier
My bill is far too much and I cannot afford to pay it	Din kling kling woten nah.
The hotel soothsayer made a false prophesy	Der gluber vizer doner Unfols-deth spikeforded
What is the matter with the porter	Wir der Quasi gaiter?
Do you serve fiery alchols?	Hip hip zum flambot
This food has **rendered us incontinent**	Diy snips hat mir pizzy pizzy gerwazzed.

HEALTH ALERTS

WINDOW EAR

FELINE LIMB SYNDROME

VATICAN NECK

POLLOCK'S KIDNEY

SHALLOW VEIN THROBBING

P·O·P

TOE DISINTEGRATION

COW TONGUE

GERMAN NASALS

RHYMING

TROPICAL PUNKING

IDLE FEELING

PRE-DEATH-JITTERING

HOLBORN FEVER

BANJO LEGS

ACQUIRED TASTE DEFICIENCY

CLUMPS

3RD LEG SYNDROME

FEELINGS

FLAMING LIPS

LAMBERTS SYMPATHY

TIDY-SPLEEN-DISEASE

DISTENDED EGO

EXTREME ARM

CHIP-EATERS-MOLAR

DENNIS-HENDERSON ACHE

COUGHING GENITALIA

BASIL'S FAULT

FAT HAIR

MISDISTRIBUTED PORES

VENUS FLU

C·A·N·O·E

ENVELOPE SPLEEN

PANDA DESERTION POX

INNER-STAINING

TOGGLES .

RESTAURANTS AND BARS (CHAINS)

THE SLODGE LODGE

WE ③ VEG

GNOODLES GNOSHERY

THE ELITE HATE KITCHEN

GRUBSKIS

PIZZA PIT

L'INVESTIGATION

LE GRANDE EXPULSION

VIVALDI'S

RADISH SHACK

BILLY BENDERS

T·R·J·RATWHACKERS

THE DARK PASSAGE

DONER TELL EVERYONE!

FIRE ~ FIRE ~ FIRE

SQUEAKERS FONDUS

LIVE EELS

WAGGY FINGERS

THE CREAMY CANTEEN

Mc TOSSWEEDS

'HORSE'

COLIN'S

L'ATTITUDE 0%

VAN DE SLUPPIES

THE BUSINESS

'SNIPPED & DIPPED'

HAM BY THE GRAMME

MAD PLATTERS

COIN OP DINER

THE GREEN STUFF

ZOLTAN & SARAH'S DIPWICHERY

TEDDY'S ALL NAZI-GRILL

THE WITH ~ INN

RELIGIOUS GROUPS IN THE AREA

CATHOLIC MASSAGE

THE JESUSEERS CHEER GROUP

SPIRITUALANIS

'SIN AGAIN, SIN BETTER'

HELLO POVERTY

THE 3RD WING OF THE TRIVIAL ORDER OF ALL THE SAINTS AND MARTYRS CHURCH OF ETERNAL GNASHING

THE FLAMING FINGER

REACTION (14)

THE SACRED MILK SHRINE

TOMB OF THE PROPHETS MATES

ALL PRAISE THE CREATURE

WIKKAN BBQ GROUP

THE MANTOVANIANS

DIET CRUSADE

WHIRL Ô WORSHIP

SOUP & A SAINT

ICON TOUCHERS

CHRISTIAN FUMBLINGS

SOUL BINGO

'PRAISIDOCIOUS' ©

LOCAL DEATH CULT

BIBLE-WIPERS

MASS IN MORSE

ON-LINE-HEALING

TAKE UP THE GOOSE OLD TESTAMENT FOWL VENERATION SERVICE.

PRIMITIVE URGES

LOTTO DIVINITY

POPE CLUB

CHURCH OF THE CUSSING AND THE SHOUTING.

TART MAKING BROTHERHOOD

HOLY SWINGS

'BLINDER!' ™

First published 2008

Redstone Press
7a St Lawrence Terrace, London W10 5SU
www.redstonepress.co.uk

Design: Julian Rothenstein
Artwork: Otis Marchbank
Production: Tim Chester
Printed in China by C & C Offset Printing

ISBN 978-1-870003-01-8

A CIP record for this book is available from the British Library

Acknowledgements
Thanks to Emma Tennant, Lucien Rothenstein, Leo Hollis

www.redstonepress.co.uk